Contents

Skills Worksheet

Concept Review

Section: Electric Charge and Force

1. **Describe** the interaction between two unlike charges.

   _____

2. **Determine** the amount by which the electric force between two charges is increased when the distance between the charges is halved.

   _____

3. **Categorize** the following as conductors or insulators:

   _____ a. salt water

   _____ b. a silver belt buckle

   _____ c. a piece of wood

   _____ d. a penny

   _____ e. a candy bar

4. **Determine** whether each charge in the diagram below is positive or negative. Indicate which charge is greater.

   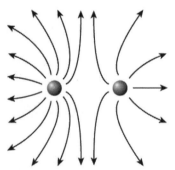

5. **Suppose** the electric field in a region points upward.

   a. **Determine** the direction of the electric force on a proton placed in the field.

   _____

   b. **Determine** the direction of the electric force on an electron placed in the field.

   _____

   c. **Compare** the accelerations of the proton and electron placed in this electric field.

   _____

   _____

Skills Worksheet

Concept Review

Section: Current

1. **State** the condition that is necessary for a charge to move in a wire.

   _____

   _____

2. **Explain** how connecting an electric device to a battery produces a current in the device.

   _____

   _____

   _____

3. **Relate** the definition of electric current to the units of current.

   _____

   _____

   _____

4. **Describe** the cause of resistance and how the resistance of a wire can be determined.

   _____

   _____

   _____

5. **Calculate** the voltage required to produce a current of 2.0 A in a wire with a resistance of 16 Ω.

   _____

6. **Calculate** the amount of current in your fingers if they touch the terminals of a 12 V battery when the resistance of your skin is 650 Ω.

   _____

7. **Compare** superconductors and semiconductors with conductors and insulators.

   _____

   _____

   _____

   _____

Skills Worksheet

Concept Review

Section: Circuits

1. **Identify** the types of elements in the schematic diagram shown below. Give the number of each type of element in the diagram.

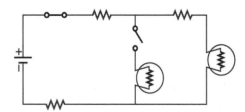

2. **Predict** which fuse would give the greatest protection against high current in a circuit—a 20 A fuse or a 30 A fuse. Explain your answer.

_____

_____

3. **Contrast** series circuits and parallel circuits.

_____

_____

_____

_____

4. **Calculate** the power of a portable radio that operates on 24 V (two 12 V batteries in series) and draws 2.2 A of current.

_____

5. **Calculate** the current drawn by a 4.0 W flashlight bulb that uses a 12 V battery.

_____

6. **Calculate** the resistance of a 45 W light bulb that has a current of 0.38 A.

_____

7. **Explain** why household appliances are almost always connected in parallel.

_____

_____

Skills Worksheet

Math Skills

Resistance

After you study each sample problem and solution, work out the practice problems on a separate sheet of paper. Write your answers in the spaces provided.

PROBLEM

A clothes dryer is equipped with an electric heater. The heater works by passing air across an electric wire that is hot because of the current in it. The wire's resistance is 10.0 Ω, and the current in the wire equals 24 A. What is the voltage across the heater wire?

SOLUTION

Step 1: **List the given and unknown values.**

> **Given:** *resistance, R* = 10.0 Ω
>
> *current, I* = 24 A
>
> **Unknown:** *voltage, V* = ? V

Step 2. **Write the equation for resistance, and rearrange it to solve for voltage.**

$$R = \frac{V}{I} \qquad\qquad V = IR$$

Step 3. **Insert the known values into the equation, and solve.**

$$V = (10.0\ \Omega) \times (24\ \text{A})$$
$$V = 240\ \text{V}$$

PRACTICE

1. A hair dryer uses a wire that is hot because of the current in it to warm the air that blows through the dryer. The resistance of this wire is 7.7 Ω. If the current through the wire equals 15.6 A, what is the voltage across the terminals of the hair dryer?

   _____

2. A battery-powered electric lantern is used as a light source for campers. The light bulb in the lantern has a resistance of 6.4 Ω. Assume the rest of the lantern's circuit has no resistance and that the current in the circuit is 0.75 A. Calculate the voltage across the terminals of the lantern's battery.

   _____

3. Some kitchen sinks are equipped with electric garbage disposals. These are units with rapidly rotating steel blades that crush and chop food so that it can be washed down the drain instead of taking up space as solid garbage. The motor of a garbage disposal has a resistance of about 25.0 Ω. If the current in the motor is 4.66 A, what is the voltage across the motor's terminals?

_____

4. A washing machine motor works because of a current of 9.80 A in a circuit with a resistance of 12.2 Ω. What is the voltage across the terminals of the motor?

_____

5. A flashlight uses three batteries of equal voltage. The batteries are connected in series, so the overall voltage of the light is equal to the sum of the voltages of each battery. If the resistance of the light bulb's filament is 3.5 Ω and the current in the filament is 1.3 A, what is the total voltage across the filament? What is the voltage across each battery?

_____

PROBLEM

An electric car is equipped with a motor that can deliver 50 hp. The voltage across the motor's terminals equals 5.0×10^2 V, and the resistance in the motor's circuit is 7.5 Ω. How large is the current in the motor?

SOLUTION

Step 1: List the given and unknown values.

> **Given:** *voltage, $V = 5.0 \times 10^2$ V*
>
> *resistance, $R = 7.5$ Ω*
>
> **Unknown:** *current, $I = ?$ A*

Step 2: Write the equation for resistance, and rearrange it to solve for current.

$$R = \frac{V}{I} \qquad I = \frac{V}{R}$$

Step 3: Insert the known values into the equation, and solve.

$$I = \frac{5.0 \times 10^2 \text{ V}}{7.5 \text{ Ω}}$$

$$I = 67 \text{ A}$$

PRACTICE

6. A quadraphonic car stereo operates on electricity provided by the car's 12-V battery. Each channel of the stereo, which feeds the electric signal to one of the stereo's four speakers, has a resistance of about 4.1 Ω. What is the current in the circuit of each stereo channel?

_____

7. When resistors are connected end to end in a circuit, they are said to be in a series. The total resistance equals the sum of all the resistances. Suppose a string of lights has 25 bulbs. Each bulb has a resistance of 8.0 Ω. If the string is plugged into a 120-V outlet, how much current is in the entire set of lights?

_____

8. A chandelier has 10 sockets, each of which holds a 60.0-W light bulb. Each light bulb has a resistance of 240 Ω. However, the chandelier is wired so that the overall resistance provided by the 10-bulb circuit is only about 24.0 Ω. If the voltage across the chandelier's circuit is 115 V, how much current is in the chandelier?

_____

9. A window-unit air conditioner has an overall resistance of 22 Ω. If the voltage across the air conditioner equals 115 V, what is the current in the air conditioner's circuit?

_____

PROBLEM

A television set is plugged into a 120-V outlet. The current in the television is equal to 0.75 A. What is the overall resistance of the television set?

SOLUTION

Step 1: List the given and unknown values.

> **Given:** *voltage, V = 120 V*
>
> *current, I = 0.75 A*
>
> **Unknown:** *resistance, R = ? Ω*

Step 2: Write the equation for resistance.

$$R = \frac{V}{I}$$

Step 3:   Insert the known values into the equation, and solve.

$$R = \frac{V}{I} = \frac{120\ V}{0.75\ A}$$

$$R = 160\ \Omega$$

PRACTICE

10. A medium-sized household oscillating fan draws 0.520 A of current when the potential difference across its motor is 120.0 V. How large is the fan's resistance?

_____

11. A refrigerator's circuit has a current equal to 0.647 A in it when the voltage across the circuit equals 116 V. What is the resistance of the circuit?

_____

MIXED PRACTICE

12. A portable, high-intensity lamp contains three bulbs with different power ratings: 150 W, 300 W, and 500 W. The resistance of each of these light bulbs decreases as the bulb's power output increases so that the 150-W bulb has a resistance of 96.0 Ω, the 300-W bulb has a resistance of 48.0 Ω, and the 500-W bulb has a resistance of 29.0 Ω. If the voltage across each bulb is 120.0 V, what is the current in each bulb?

_____

13. You have probably heard that high voltages are more dangerous than low voltages. To understand this, assume that your body has a resistance of $1.0 \times 10^5\ \Omega$. What voltages would have to be across your body to produce a current of 5.0 mA (milliamps, or 0.001 A), which would cause a tingling feeling; 10.0 mA, which would be a fatal amount of current; and 1.0 A?

_____

14. While in another country, you should always find out the voltage that is used in that country before you plug in an appliance. To understand the reason for this precaution, calculate the resistance of a laptop computer that is designed to draw 3.0 A at 115 V. Then, calculate the current that the same computer would draw if you plugged it into a 220-V outlet, which is common in countries other than the United States.

_____

Skills Worksheet

Math Skills

Electric Power

After you study each sample problem and solution, work out the practice problems on a separate sheet of paper. Write your answers in the spaces provided.

PROBLEM

An alarm clock uses 5.0 W of electric power. If the clock is plugged into a 120-V outlet, what electric current is in the clock's circuit?

SOLUTION

Step 1: List the given and unknown values.

Given: *voltage, V = 120 V*

power, P = 5.0 W

Unknown: *current, I = ? A*

Step 2: Write the equation for electric power, and rearrange it to solve for current.

$$P = VI \qquad I = \frac{P}{V}$$

Step 3: Insert the known values into the equation, and solve.

$$I = \frac{5.0 \text{ W}}{120 \text{ V}}$$

$$I = 4.2 \times 10^{-2} \text{ A}$$

PRACTICE

1. The headlights of an automobile have two power ratings: 45 W for the low beam and 65 W for the high beam. How much is the current in the headlight filament of a headlight bulb for both of these settings when 12 V is provided by the car battery?

_____

2. The heating coils of an electric stove are made of a high-resistance material so that the electricity that passes through the coils causes them to become red hot within a minute. The smaller coil draws 1,250 W of power, while the larger coil draws 2,100 W. The voltage provided across each coil is 240 V. What is the current in each coil?

_____

3. An electric mixer draws 200.0 W of power. If the mixer is plugged into an outlet across a voltage of 115 V, what current is in the mixer's circuit?

_____

4. A bus built in 1905 used electricity produced by a gasoline-powered generator. The generator provided 33.6 kW of power to the bus. If the voltage across the electric motor was 440 V, what was the current in the motor?

_____

5. Alternating current is used today because its voltage can be easily changed by a device called a transformer. Transformers are used both to increase the voltage of electricity, so that it can travel long distances, and to decrease the voltage, so that the electricity can be used in your house with relative safety. If the voltage across two wires is raised to 2.5×10^5 V, what is its current if 1.0×10^5 of power is provided?

_____

PROBLEM

A high-intensity portable lantern is powered by several batteries that are connected in series. The lantern's bulb uses 96 W of power, while the current in the lantern is 4.0 A. Assuming that there is no power loss in the circuit, what is the total voltage of the batteries?

SOLUTION

Step 1: **List the given and unknown values.**

> **Given:** *power, P* = 96 W
>
> *current, I* = 4.0 A
>
> **Unknown:** *voltage, V* = ? V

Step 2: **Write the equation for power, and rearrange it to solve for voltage.**

$$P = VI \qquad V = \frac{P}{I}$$

Step 3: **Insert the known values into the equation, and solve.**

$$V = \frac{96 \text{ W}}{4.0 \text{ A}}$$

$$V = 24 \text{ V}$$

PRACTICE

6. A nightlight uses 4.00 W of power when plugged into an outlet. Assume that the only resistance in the circuit is provided by the light bulb's filament. The current in the circuit is 3.40×10^{-2} A. What is the voltage across the filament?

7. A portable power source is available for travelers who need electricity for appliances. The power source provides 54 W of power to operate an air compressor for inflating tires. This compressor draws 4.5 A of current when connected to the power supply. What is the voltage across the compressor?

8. A certain high-speed train is powered by 64 electric motors—one motor for each axle of each car. The power output of each motor is 185 kW. The current provided to each motor from overhead power lines is 7.4 A. What is the voltage across each motor?

9. A particular laser developed in 1995 at the University of Rochester, in New York, produced a beam of light that lasted for about one-billionth of a second. The power output of this beam was 6.0×10^{13} W. Assume that all of the electrical power was converted into light and that 8.0×10^{6} A of current was needed to produce this beam. How large was the voltage that produced the current?

10. Fuel cells are chemical cells that combine hydrogen and oxygen gas to produce electrical energy. In recent years, a fuel cell has been developed that can generate 1.06×10^{4} of power. If the cell produces a current of 16.3 A, what is the voltage across the cell?

PROBLEM

A generator produces electricity with a voltage of 2.5×10^{4} V and a current of 20.0 A. How much power does the generator produce?

SOLUTION

Step 1: List the given and unknown values.

> **Given:** *voltage, $V = 2.5 \times 10^{4}$ V*
>
> *current, $I = 20.0$ A*
>
> **Unknown:** *power, $P = ?$ W*

Step 2: Write the equation for power.

> $P = VI$

| Math Skills *continued*

Step 3: **Insert the known values into the equation, and solve.**

$$P = (2.5 \times 10^4 \text{ V}) \times (20.0 \text{ A})$$
$$P = 5.0 \times 10^5 \text{ W}$$

PROBLEM

A computer with a resistance of 57.5 Ω has a power input of 230.0 W. Calculate the voltage across and current in the computer, using the formulas relating power to resistance.

SOLUTION

Step 1: **List the given and unknown values.**

Given: *power, P* = 230.0 W

resistance, R = 57.5 Ω

Unknown: *voltage, V* = ? V

current, I = ? A

Step 2: **Write the equations for power in terms of resistance, and rearrange them to solve for voltage and current.**

$$P = VI = V \times \frac{V}{R} = \frac{V^2}{R}$$
$$V = \sqrt{PR}$$
$$P = VI = (IR) \times I = I^2R$$
$$I = \sqrt{\frac{P}{R}}$$

Step 3: Insert the known values into the equations, and solve.

$$V = \sqrt{(230.0 \text{ W}) \times (57.5 \text{ Ω})}$$
$$V = 115 \text{ V}$$
$$I = \sqrt{\frac{230.0 \text{ W}}{57.5 \text{ Ω}}}$$
$$I = 2.00 \text{ A}$$

PRACTICE

11. A current of 5.83 A is used to produce the microwave radiation in a microwave oven. If the voltage across the oven is 120 V, how much power does the oven use?

_____

12. A vacuum cleaner's motor has a voltage of 120 V across its terminals and a current of 12 A. How much power does the vacuum cleaner use?

_____

| Math Skills *continued*

13. A refrigerator uses a current of 0.62 A and a voltage of 116 V. How much power does the refrigerator use?

_____

14. An electric sports car was developed several years ago at Texas A & M University, in College Station, Texas. If the voltage required to operate the car was 720 V and the resistance was 0.30 V, how much power was needed for the car to run? (Hint: Express current in terms of voltage and resistance, and substitute this into the power equation.)

_____

MIXED PRACTICE

15. Electric power is often produced by a gas-powered generator. Suppose one of these generators has a power output of about 7.50×10^4 W. If the generator produces a voltage of 114 V, how much current is in the generator?

_____

16. Several appliances in a house contribute to the home's overall energy consumption. If a toaster ($R = 18.0\ \Omega$) an air conditioner ($R = 24.0\ \Omega$), and an electric lamp ($R = 192\ \Omega$) are all plugged into 120.0-V outlets, what is the power use of each appliance? What is the overall power use?

_____

17. There are 17 generators at Hoover Dam, each of which produces electricity with a voltage of 1.65×10^4 V and a current of 7.37×10^3A. What is each generator's power output?

_____

18. One of the problems with transmitting electricity is that the resistance of the wire causes some energy to be transferred away as heat. This energy loss is equal to $I^2 R$. The loss can be reduced if the voltage can be increased so that the current decreases. Only alternating current can undergo this voltage increase, which is why AC is used for producing most electricity. Consider a power plant that produces 5.00×10^5 W of electricity. The wire has a resistance of $1.00 \times 10^5\ \Omega$. What is the power loss if the voltage is transmitted at 2.50×10^2 V? at 2.50×10^5 V?

_____

19. Power from mechanical work is often converted into electrical energy. Suppose you have a generator connected to a waterwheel that is turned by a waterfall. The waterfall is 25 m high, with 980 kg of water falling each second onto the waterwheel. If all of this mechanical energy is converted to electricity, how much power is generated? If the generated current is 20.0 A, what is the voltage?

_____

Skills Worksheet   **CONNECTION TO SOCIAL STUDIES**

Cross-Disciplinary

Incandescent Light Bulbs

Read the following paragraphs, and complete the exercises below.

In 1752, Ben Franklin with his kite experiment demonstrated that lightning is related to electricity. Experiments to understand electricity continued, and many electric devices were invented. In 1879, Thomas Edison invented a system of electric lighting that would eventually bring electric lights into homes. The key to Edison's electric lighting system was the incandescent light bulb.

Incandescent light bulbs are glass bulbs from which all air has been pumped out. The air is replaced with chemically inactive gas, like nitrogen. The glow from an incandescent light bulb comes from the filament, a little wire, which is often visible, inside bulbs. Today, the common material for filaments is tungsten. When electricity flows through the filament of an incandescent bulb, the tungsten wire gets hot enough to glow and give off light. Atoms of tungsten evaporate from the white-hot filament. The escaped tungsten atoms collect on the glass and darken it. Over time, the filament grows thin and eventually breaks.

HALOGEN BULBS

A variation of the incandescent light bulb is the halogen bulb. Gases inside halogen bulbs are chemically active. Each time a tungsten atom leaves the filament, halogen molecules inside the glass pick it up and return it to the filament. Redepositing the tungsten atoms back on the filament allows the filament to last longer. These halogen molecules can do this job only if the glass of the bulb is allowed to get extremely hot—much hotter than incandescent bulbs get.

EXERCISES

1. Which type of light bulb, ordinary incandescent or halogen, would last longer? Explain your answer.

   _____

   _____

   _____

   _____

2. What causes the tungsten atoms to evaporate from the filament?

   _____

   _____

   _____

   _____

Cross-Disciplinary

Electric Eels

Read the following paragraphs, and complete the exercises below.

Electric eels are found in the Amazon, Orinoco, and other muddy rivers in the tropical regions of South America. They grow as large as 2.75 m (9 ft) long and weigh up to 22 kg (49 lb). Electric eels are one of the few animals that can make, store, and discharge electricity. Electric eels use this electricity to navigate, communicate, stun or kill their prey, and defend themselves.

ELECTROPLAQUES

You can understand how an eel generates electricity by imagining its body as a series of batteries. An eel's body contains an organ that produces electricity. This organ is made up of 5,000 to 6,000 special muscle cells called electroplaques. The electroplaques are lined up like cells in a dry battery. Each electroplaque produces only a small voltage. However, eels can activate all of their electroplaques at the same time and produce a much higher voltage. When electric eels discharge electricity, the current flows either from head to tail or in the opposite direction. The more electroplaques that are activated, the greater the discharge.

Electric eels have more than one level of discharge. They generally discharge about 25 to 75 V, but when they discharge from all the electroplaque cells at the same time, they can jolt the receiver with as much as 500 to 650 V of electricity.

EXERCISES

1. Would the size of an electric eel influence the amount of volts that it could discharge? Explain your answer.

   _____

   _____

2. How does the highest discharge of an electric eel compare with the voltage that comes out of a normal wall socket?

   _____

   _____

3. Would it be dangerous for a human to be in the water near an electric eel that discharged a jolt of electricity to stun a large fish? Explain your answer.

   _____

   _____

Skills Worksheet

Cross-Disciplinary

Rechargeable Ni-Cd Batteries

Read the following paragraphs, and complete the exercises below.

Rechargeable nickel-cadmium batteries are used in many portable appliances, such as cordless phones, radios, video cameras, and emergency medical equipment. In a battery of this type, the electrodes are nickel oxide, NiO_2, and cadmium metal, Cd.

THE CHEMISTRY OF A NICKEL-CADMIUM BATTERY

In a rechargeable nickel-cadmium battery, as in any battery, there are two electrodes. The cadmium electrode is the battery's *anode,* where cadmium gives up electrons—in an *oxidation* reaction—and forms cadmium hydroxide. The nickel oxide electrode is the battery's *cathode,* where nickel oxide gains electrons—in a *reduction* reaction—and forms nickel hydroxide. The overall chemical reaction is:

$$Cd + NiO_2 + 2H_2O \rightarrow Cd(OH)_2 + Ni(OH)_2$$

WHY NICKEL-CADMIUM BATTERIES ARE ECONOMICAL

Nickel-cadmium batteries are more expensive initially than regular batteries. However, they are more economical in the long run. When the batteries are placed in a charger, nickel oxide and cadmium can be easily regenerated, making the batteries almost as good as new. With this process, it is possible to recharge the batteries hundreds of times before they finally wear out.

EXERCISES

1. When is battery power more useful than plugging an appliance into an outlet?

_____

_____

2. In the battery described above, nickel oxide gains electrons. Where do these electrons come from?

_____

3. Regular batteries are less expensive than rechargeable batteries. How can it be more expensive in the long run to use regular batteries?

_____

_____

Skills Worksheet

Cross-Disciplinary

Recording Electricity in the Brain

Read the following paragraphs, and complete the exercises below.

The brain activity and its function is carried out by nerve cells such as neurons. Neurons use chemicals to produce electrical signals. These signals are passed from neuron to neuron along pathways called circuits. When the brain is active, the neurons in the brain show intense electrical activity.

The electroencephalogram machine, sometimes called an electroencephalograph, is used to detect and record electrical activity in the brain. To administer the test, a medical technician attaches a number of small electrodes to a person's scalp. The electrodes are receptors through which electric current from the brain and scalp is gathered and sent to the machine. The electrical activity of the brain is recorded on paper tape. The tape moves forward under ink pens that move back and forth with each change in the brain's electrical activity. The wavelike patterns in these recordings are called brain waves. The entire record is called an electroencephalogram, or EEG.

MEDICAL USES OF THE EEG

The most common medical use of EEGs is to diagnose and study epilepsy. The brains of people who have epilepsy have excessive electrical activity that sometimes interferes with normal brain function. The interference can result in seizures. By studying a person's EEG, a physician can determine the parts of the brain that are responsible for causing the seizures.

EEGs are also used to study sleep. Research using EEG machines shows that the pattern of brain waves changes as a person falls asleep. The changes continue as the person moves through the various stages of sleep and returns to wakefulness.

EXERCISES

1. What is likely to happen to brain waves when you relax?

_____

_____

2. What happens to brain waves during epilepsy?

_____

_____

3. How do neurons communicate with each other?

_____

Skills Worksheet

Cross-Disciplinary

Electric Shock: Caution!

Read the following paragraphs, and complete the exercises below.

Current, voltage, and *resistance* are three basic terms used to describe electricity. Current is the rate at which electricity flows. Voltage is the force that causes the electricity to flow. Resistance is the property that slows the flow of electricity through a conducting material.

THE PATH OF LEAST RESISTANCE

Electricity always travels the path of least resistance. The path of least resistance is a good conductor, such as a metal, any wet material, or the human body. Dry skin gives some resistance to the flow of electricity. However, if the skin is wet—especially from sweat—the resistance drops dramatically.

ELECTRIC SHOCK CAN HAVE A WIDE RANGE OF EFFECTS

If you touch a "live" wire while you are touching the ground or standing on another conductor that is touching the ground, electricity will flow through you and you will be shocked. Electric shock can be a mild tingle or a deadly jolt. The effect is determined by how much current flows through the body and where it goes. The small amount of electricity used by one Christmas tree bulb can kill a person if it passes through a vital organ.

EXERCISES

1. Two children riding bicycles come to a downed power-line pole that blocks their way. The line is not broken, and a small bird sitting on the line seems fine. Can the children assume that the line is safe for them to pick up and move aside? Explain your answer.

   _____

   _____

2. A certain electric tool comes with a ground wire that users should attach to a path to the ground. How is the ground wire a safety precaution?

   _____

   _____

3. An electric wire has burned through and fallen on top of the clothes dryer. If you are careful not to touch the wire, would it be safe to open the dryer door to remove the clothing? Explain your answer.

   _____

   _____

Skills Worksheet

Cross-Disciplinary

Battery Issues

Read the following paragraphs, and complete the exercises below.

Many batteries are nonrechargeable—once they run out of power, they cannot be recharged. Rechargeable batteries cost a bit more but last longer because they can be recharged. Eventually they must be discarded too. Some batteries contain hazardous substances; therefore, proper disposal depends on the type of substances that are present in the battery.

Alkaline batteries, commonly used in flashlights, are nonrechargeable batteries. They are nonhazardous and can be thrown in the garbage. Button batteries are small, disk-shaped batteries used to power many watches, calculators, and hearing aids. Button batteries usually contain mercury, silver, or lithium. Used button batteries should be returned to the manufacturer so they can be properly discarded.

RECHARGEABLE BATTERIES

Nickel-cadmium (Ni-Cd) batteries, the most common rechargeable batteries, are used in cellular phones, electronic equipment, and some toys. Ni-Cd batteries last about 700 charge cycles. These batteries contain cadmium, a dangerous metal. Used Ni-Cd batteries should be recycled or handled as hazardous waste.

Nickel-metal-hydride (NiMH) batteries are another type of rechargeable battery. This kind of battery is used in notebook computers, cameras, and other equipment. Nickel-metal-hydrides are environmentally friendly and contain only nontoxic metals. They last for about 400 charge cycles.

EXERCISES

1. Would rechargeable or nonrechargeable batteries be most economical? Explain your answer.

   _____

2. Which type of battery is best for the environment? Explain your answer.

   _____

   _____

3. Where could you learn how to dispose of a battery?

   _____

   _____

   _____

Assessment

Pretest

Electricity

1. Describe the parts of an atom. What are the outermost particles of an atom?

_____

_____

_____

2. Describe the difference between a material that is a good conductor of electricity and a material that has a high resistance.

_____

_____

_____ 3. Any change in an object's motion is called
   a. momentum.   c. force.
   b. acceleration.   d. velocity.

_____ 4. Changes in an object's motion are caused by
   a. a balanced force.   c. an unbalanced force.
   b. an acceleration.   d. opposing forces.

_____ 5. The gravitational force between two objects depends on the
   a. volume of the objects.   c. mass of the objects.
   b. speed of the objects.   d. charge of the objects.

6. Describe why you might receive a small shock when you walk across a rug in sneakers on a dry day and then grab a doorknob.

_____

7. Describe the energy transformations that take place when a ball rolls down a hill. How does this demonstrate the conservation of energy?

_____

_____

8. Name three household items that use a battery as a source of electric current.

_____

_____

_____

Assessment

Quiz

Section: Electric Charge and Force

In the space provided, write the letter of the term or phrase that best completes each statement or best answers each question.

_____ 1. Positive charges _____ one another.
   - a. attract
   - b. cancel
   - c. repel
   - d. join

_____ 2. The electric force between two objects _____ when the distance between them decreases.
   - a. increases
   - b. decreases
   - c. remains constant
   - d. None of the above

_____ 3. Which of the following is a negatively charged particle?
   - a. proton
   - b. electron
   - c. coulomb
   - d. neutron

_____ 4. Electric field lines show the strength and _____ of an electric field.
   - a. polarization
   - b. direction
   - c. temperature
   - d. friction

In the space provided, write the letter of the term or phrase that best matches each description.

_____ 5. a material that allows electric charges to move easily

_____ 6. SI unit of electric charge

_____ 7. alignment of charges at the surface of an object producing an induced charge

_____ 8. the force of attraction or repulsion between objects due to charge

_____ 9. a material that does not easily transfer electric charge

_____ 10. an electrical property of matter that creates electric and magnetic forces and interactions

   - a. electrical insulator
   - b. electrical conductor
   - c. electric force
   - d. polarization
   - e. coulomb
   - f. electric charge

Assessment

Quiz

Section: Current

In the space provided, write the letter of the term or phrase that best completes each statement or best answers each question.

_____ 1. An electric cell is a source of electric current because of a
_____ between the terminals.
   a. resistance   c. semiconductor
   b. light bulb   d. potential difference

_____ 2. A(n) _____ is a solution that conducts electricity.
   a. electrode   b. voltage   c. terminal   d. electrolyte

_____ 3. The rate at which charges move through a conductor is called
   a. voltage.   c. current.
   b. resistance.   d. electrical potential energy.

_____ 4. Conventional current is defined as the movement of
   a. positive charge.   c. negative charge.
   b. variable charge.   d. net charge.

_____ 5. _____ is the opposition posed by a material to the flow of
current.
   a. Voltage   b. Charge   c. Resistance   d. Ampere

_____ 6. Current is produced when charges are accelerated by an electric field to
move to a position of lower
   a. temperature.   c. concentration.
   b. potential energy.   d. kinetic energy.

_____ 7. Calculate the resistance of a bulb that draws 0.6 A of current with a
potential difference of 3 V.
   a. 0.2 Ω   b. 1.8 Ω   c. 5 Ω   d. 15 Ω

_____ 8. Which of the following has the lowest resistance?
   a. semiconductor   c. conductor
   b. superconductor   d. insulator

_____ 9. A 6.0-V battery is connected to a 24-Ω resistor. What is the current in
the resistor?
   a. 0.25 A   b. 4.0 A   c. 18 A   d. 144 A

_____ 10. In most cases, increasing the temperature of an object will
_____ its resistance.
   a. increase   c. have no effect on
   b. decrease   d. nullify

Assessment

Quiz

Section: Circuits

In the space provided, write the letter of the term or phrase that best completes each statement or best answers each question.

_____ 1. Individual components in a parallel circuit experience the same
        a. voltage.   c. power.
        b. current.   d. dissipation.

_____ 2. A device connected to a 120-V outlet has 2.0 A of current in it. What is the power of this device?
        a. 48 W   c. 240 W
        b. 60 W   d. 480 W

_____ 3. A circuit breaker acts as a switch creating a(n) _____ circuit when current is too high.
        a. closed   c. open
        b. series   d. parallel

_____ 4. What voltage is required to pass 0.5 A of current through a 4.5-W bulb?
        a. 0.11 V   c. 3 V
        b. 2.25 V   d. 9 V

In the space provided, write the letter of the term or phrase that best matches each description.

_____ 5. a circuit in which two or more paths are connected to the voltage source

_____ 6. a device that contains a metal strip that melts when a certain current is exceeded

_____ 7. a low-resistance alternative pathway for current to travel in a circuit

_____ 8. a device used to open or close an electric circuit

_____ 9. a circuit in which the components form a single path

_____ 10. the rate at which electrical work is done

a. switch
b. series circuit
c. parallel circuit
d. electric power
e. fuse
f. short circuit

Assessment   **TEST A**

Chapter Test

Electricity

In the space provided, write the letter of the term or phase that best completes each statement or best answers each question.

_____ 1. There is a repulsive force between two charged objects when
   a. their charges are of unlike sign.
   b. they have the same number of protons.
   c. their charges are of like sign.
   d. they have the same number of electrons.

_____ 2. Electric force varies depending on the
   a. charge and distance between charged objects.
   b. charge and mass of charged objects.
   c. height and mass of charged objects.
   d. mass and distance between charged objects.

_____ 3. Batteries typically have
   a. two positive terminals.
   b. two negative terminals.
   c. one positive and one negative terminal.
   d. no terminals.

_____ 4. An electric current is produced when charges are accelerated by an electric field to move to a position of potential energy that is
   a. higher.   c. equal.
   b. lower.   d. infinite.

_____ 5. Resistance is caused by
   a. internal friction.   c. proton charge.
   b. electron charge.   d. kinetic energy.

_____ 6. The SI unit of resistance is the
   a. volt.   c. ohm.
   b. ampere.   d. joule.

_____ 7. What is the potential difference across a resistor that dissipates 5.00 W of power and has a current of 5.0 A?
   a. 1.0 V   c. 125 V
   b. 4.00 V   d. 0.20 V

_____ 8. There is a potential difference of 12 V across a resistor with 0.25 A of current in it. The resistance of the resistor is
   a. 48 Ω.   c. 12 Ω.
   b. 24 Ω.   d. 0.021 Ω.

| Chapter Test *continued*

_____ 9. A resistor has a resistance of 280 Ω. How much current is in the resistor if there is a potential difference of 120 V across the resistor?
  a. 160 A   c. 0.12 A
  b. 0.43 A   d. 2.3 A

_____ 10. What happens to the resistance of a superconductor when its temperature drops below the critical temperature?
  a. Resistance increases.
  b. Resistance doubles.
  c. Resistance drops to zero.
  d. Resistance is reduced by one half.

_____ 11. If a lamp is measured to have a resistance of 120 Ω when it operates at a power of 1.00×10^2 W, what is the potential difference across the lamp?
  a. 110 V   c. 0.913 V
  b. 120 V   d. 220 V

_____ 12. A microwave draws 5.0 A when it is connected to a 120-V outlet. If electrical energy costs $0.090/kW • h, what is the cost of running the microwave for exactly 6 hours?
  a. $2.70   c. $0.72
  b. $1.60   d. $0.32

_____ 13. What happens to the overall resistance of a circuit when too many appliances are connected across a 120-V outlet?
  a. Resistance is increased.   c. Resistance is decreased.
  b. Resistance remains the same. d. Resistance is zero.

Read each question, and write your response in the space provided.

14. What is charging by friction?

_____

_____

_____

_____

_____

15. In the figure shown below, why do only half of the lines originating from the positive charge terminate on the negative charge?

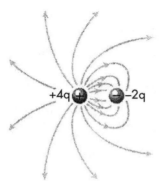

_____

_____

16. What determines the electrical potential energy of a charge?

_____

17. A resistor has a resistance of 1.8 Ω. How much current is in the resistor if there is a potential difference of 3.0 V across the resistor?

_____

18. Which bulb(s) will have a current in the schematic diagram below?

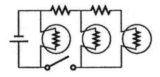

_____

19. Does the schematic diagram below represent a series or parallel circuit?

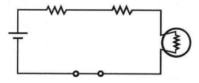

_____

20. Does the wiring in your house use series or parallel circuits? Explain your answer.

_____

_____

Assessment   **TEST B**

Chapter Test

Electricity

In the space provided, write the letter of the term or phase that best completes each statement or best answers each question.

_____ 1. There is an attractive force between two charged objects when
  a. their charges are of unlike sign.
  b. they have the same number of protons.
  c. their charges are of like sign.
  d. they have the same number of electrons.

_____ 2. When there is an equal amount of positive and negative charges on an object, the object is
  a. positively charged.   c. neutral.
  b. negatively charged.   d. supercharged.

_____ 3. The electric force between charged objects is
  a. attractive only.   c. either attractive or repulsive.
  b. repulsive only.   d. neither attractive nor repulsive.

_____ 4. Every charged particle produces a(n)
  a. negative charge.   c. magnetic field.
  b. positive charge.   d. electric field.

_____ 5. When compared to a −2 charge, there are
  a. an equal number of field lines pointing inward toward a +4 charge.
  b. twice as many field lines pointing inward toward a +4 charge.
  c. twice as many field lines pointing outward from a +4 charge.
  d. half as many field lines pointing outward from a +4 charge.

_____ 6. Potential difference is measured in
  a. amperes.   c. coulombs.
  b. volts.   d. joules.

_____ 7. Current is the rate at which charges move through a(n)
  a. conductor.   c. voltage.
  b. insulator.   d. joule.

_____ 8. A flashlight bulb with a potential difference of 4.5 V across its filament has a power output of 8.0 W. How much current is in the bulb filament?
  a. 3.7 A   b. 1.8 A   c. 0.23 A   d. 0.56 A

_____ 9. A 13-Ω resistor has 0.050 A of current in it. What is the potential difference across the resistor?
  a. 6.5 V   c. 0.065 V
  b. 0.65 V   d. 0.0065 V

| Chapter Test *continued*

_____ 10. A set of electric trains are powered by a 9-V battery. What is the resistance of the trains if they draw 3.0 A of current?
    a. 3 Ω   c. 27 Ω
    b. 0.03 Ω   d. 2.7 Ω

_____ 11. An electric toaster has a power rating of 1,100 W at 110 V. What is the resistance of the heating coil?
    a. 7.5 Ω   c. 10 Ω
    b. 9.0 Ω   d. 11 Ω

_____ 12. A color television draws about 2.5 A when it is connected to a 120-V outlet. Assuming electrical energy costs $0.060 per kW • h, what is the cost of running the television for exactly 8 hours?
    a. $1.44   c. $0.14
    b. $0.03   d. $0.30

_____ 13. A device that protects a circuit from current overload is called a
    a. resistor.   c. circuit breaker.
    b. capacitor.   d. closed circuit.

Read each question, and write your response in the space provided.

14. What is charging by contact?

_____

_____

_____

15. How does the electric force between two charged objects depend on distance?

_____

_____

_____

16. A 180-Ω resistor has 0.10 A of current in it. What is the potential difference across the resistor?

_____

17. What is resistance in a conductor?

_____

_____

_____

18. Is a current flowing in the schematic diagram below? Explain your answer.

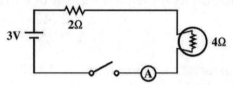

_____

19. Does the schematic diagram below represent a series or parallel circuit?

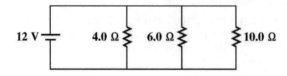

_____

20. You can pick up static electricity by walking on a wool rug in leather-soled shoes. Explain why you are then negatively charged and what happens when you grab for a metal object such as a doorknob.

_____

_____

_____

_____

Assessment   **GUIDED READING DEVELOPMENT**

Standardized Test Practice

Read the passage below and answer the questions that follow.

In 1848, gold was discovered at Sutter's Mill in California. Once the gold strike was confirmed, a mad rush <u>ensued</u>. Nearly 100,000 people flocked to the state in 1849, leaving their homes in the hopes of striking it rich in California.

Throughout history, gold has been one of the most highly sought after materials because of its limited supply, malleability, durability, and reflective brilliance. Gold is also the best electrical conductor. Gold provides a superb pathway for an electric current. This is why the high-tech industry uses gold circuits inside computers.

But why use gold in computers rather than copper? All electrical conductors generate heat, which is harmful to computer components. However, metals that conduct electricity well have lower resistance and generate less heat than metals that do not conduct electricity as well. As the best electrical conductor, gold has the lowest resistance and generates the least heat. This helps keep the temperature down inside the computer.

In the space provided, write the letter of the term or phrase that best completes each statement or best answers each question.

_____ 1. In this passage, the word ensued means
         A transcended.   C followed.
         B flourished.   D prospered.

_____ 2. Based on the information in the passage, which of the following is a FACT?
         A Copper has more resistance than gold.
         B A large amount of gold is found inside every computer.
         C Gold produces a substantial amount of heat.
         D The supply of gold is virtually limitless, making it an ideal metal for computer wiring.

_____ 3. Based on the information in the passage, what is the most likely reason people in the California gold rush were called "forty-niners"?
         A An ounce of gold sold for $49.
         B It is a cool name for a team mascot.
         C Forty-nine thousand people moved to California.
         D The name is based on the year of the gold rush.

_____ 4. The author probably wrote this passage to
         A trace the history of gold.
         B describe the reasons for gold-rush fever.
         C state some examples of gold's benefits.
         D explain the inner circuitry of computers.

Inquiry Lab   **DATASHEET**

A Simple Circuit

MATERIALS

For each group

• battery, D-cell
• flashlight
• foil, aluminum
• wire, electrical

PROCEDURE

You can investigate electricity by using the parts of a simple flashlight. Use the bulb and battery from a flashlight and some wire or aluminum foil to make the bulb light. Try connecting the light bulb to the battery in several different ways.

QUESTIONS TO GET YOU STARTED

1. Which method caused the bulb to light? Why did that method work?

_____

_____

_____

2. Which method did not cause the bulb to light? Why didn't that method work?

_____

_____

_____

Quick Lab   **DATASHEET**

Charging Objects

MATERIALS

For each group

• comb, plastic
• paper, tissue

PROCEDURE

1. Tear a sheet of tissue paper into small pieces, and pile the pieces on a table.
2. Use a plastic comb to vigorously comb your hair.
3. Use the comb to pick up the pieces of tissue.

ANALYSIS

1. Are the plastic comb and tissue paper conductors or insulators?

_____

_____

_____

2. What happens to the charges in the comb, tissue, and your hair?

_____

_____

_____

3. What would happen if you held the comb near your hair?

_____

_____

_____

Name _____ Class _____ Date _____

Quick Lab   **DATASHEET**

Using a Lemon as a Cell

MATERIALS

For each group

- copper, strip
- different metals, strips
- galvanometer
- lemon

- knife
- wire, insulated copper
- wire strippers
- zinc, strip

SAFETY

PROCEDURE

1. Using a knife, make two parallel cuts 6 cm apart along the middle of a juicy lemon. Insert a copper strip into one of the cuts and a zinc strip of the same size into the other.

2. Cut two equal lengths of insulated copper wire. Use wire strippers to remove the insulation from both ends of each wire. Connect one end of each wire to one of the terminals of a galvanometer.

3. Touch the free end of one wire to the copper strip in the lemon. Touch the free end of the other wire to the zinc strip. Record the galvanometer reading for the zinc-copper cell in the data table below.

4. Replace the strips of copper and zinc with equally sized strips of different metals. Record the galvanometer readings for each pair of electrodes in the data table below.

ANALYSIS

1. Which pair of electrodes resulted in the largest current?

_____

_____

2. Use the table below to record your results.

Metals used in cell	Galvanometer reading (V)
Zinc-copper	

Name _____ Class _____ Date _____

Inquiry Lab   **DATASHEET**

How Can Materials Be Classified by Resistance?

MATERIALS

For each group

- alligator clips (2)
- base holder
- battery, 6 V
- bulb, flashlight
- cardboard, strip
- chalk, piece
- cork, strip
- dowel, wooden
- hooks, metal (2)

- key, brass
- nail, aluminum
- nail, iron
- spoon, plastic
- stirring rod, glass
- wire, copper
- wire leads (2)
- wood, small block

SAFETY

PROCEDURE

1. Construct a conductivity tester like the one pictured in the text. First, screw two metal hooks into a block of wood.

2. Create a circuit using three wire leads with alligator clips, a 6 V battery, and a flashlight bulb in a base holder, as the diagram shows.

3. Collect some or all of the following materials to test: a glass stirring rod, an iron nail, a wooden dowel, a copper wire, a piece of chalk, a strip of cardboard, a plastic spoon, an aluminum nail, a brass key, and a strip of cork.

4. Test the conductivity of the materials by laying each object, one at a time, across the hooks of the conductivity tester.

| How Can Materials Be Classified by Resistance? *continued*

ANALYSIS

1. What happens to the conductivity tester if a material is a good conductor?

   _____

   _____

2. Which materials were good conductors? Which materials were poor conductors?

   _____

   _____

   _____

   _____

   _____

3. Explain your results in terms of resistance.

   _____

   _____

   _____

   _____

   _____

Skills Practice Lab   **DATASHEET A**

Constructing Electric Circuits

The current that flows through an electric circuit depends on voltage and resistance. All these factors are dependent on one another. In this lab, you will make circuits using different configurations of resistors and batteries to see how the voltage and current depend on them.

WHAT YOU'LL DO

Construct parallel and series circuits.

Predict voltage and current by using the resistance law.

Measure voltage, current, and resistance.

WHAT YOU'LL NEED

- battery, dry-cell
- battery holder
- multimeter

- resistors (2)
- tape, masking
- wires, connecting (3)

SAFETY

PROCEDURE

Preparing for Your Experiment

1. In this laboratory exercise, you will use an instrument called a *multimeter* to measure voltage, current, and resistance.
   - Your teacher will demonstrate how to use the multimeter to make each type of measurement.
2. As you read the steps listed below, look at the diagrams for help making the measurements.
   - Write down your predictions and measurements in the space provided, and then in your lab notebook.
   - **CAUTION:** Handle the wires only where they are insulated.

| Constructing Electric Circuits *continued*

Circuits with a Single Resistor

3. Using the multimeter, measure the resistance in ohms of one of the resistors.

_____

   • Write the resistance on a small piece of masking tape
   • Tape it to the resistor.
   • Measure the resistance in ohms of the other resistor.

_____

   • Write the resistance on a small piece of masking tape
   • Tape it to the resistor.

4. Predict the current in amps that will be in a circuit made of one of the resistors and one battery.
   • The equation for resistance is $R = V/I$.
   • To solve for current, you must rearrange the equation: $I = V/R$.
   • In the equation, I = current in amperes (A).
   • In the equation, V = volts. (**Hint:** Look at your battery. The label on the battery should tell you the voltage.)
   • In the equation, R = resistance in ohms (Ω). Look at your results in step 3, above.
   • What do you believe the current in amps will be for the first resistor using the equation $I = V/R$?

   • Record your prediction for the first resistor.

_____

   • What do you believe the current in amps will be for the second resistor using the equation $I = V/R$?

   • Record your prediction for the second resistor.

_____

5. Test your predictions.
  • Build a circuit using your first resistor and one battery.

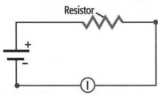

  • Use the multimeter. What is the current in amps in the circuit made of your first resistor and one battery?

  _____

  • Was your prediction correct?

  _____

  • Build a circuit using your second resistor and one battery.
  • Use the multimeter. What is the current in amps in the circuit made of your second resistor and one battery?

  _____

  • Was your prediction correct?

  _____

Circuits with Two Resistors in Series

6. Measure the total resistance across both resistors when they are connected in series.

  • Look at the resistances you found for each resistor in step 3.
  • To get the total resistance, add the resistance for the first resistor to the resistance for the second resistor.

  _____

Constructing Electric Circuits *continued*

7. Predict the current that will be in a circuit made of one battery and both resistors in series.

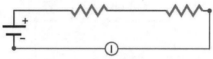

- The equation for resistance is $R = V/I$.
- To solve for current, you must rearrange the equation: $I = V/R$.
- In the equation, I = current in amperes (A).
- In the equation, V = volts of the single battery.
- In the equation, R = total resistance in ohms (Ω). Look at your results in step 6, above.
- What do you believe the current in amps will be using one battery and both resistors in series, using the equation $I = V/R$?

_____

- Build a circuit using both of your resistors and one battery.
- Use the multimeter. What is the current in amps in the circuit you made?

_____

- Was your prediction correct?

_____

Constructing Electric Circuits *continued*

8. Predict the voltage across each of the resistors in the circuit you just built.
  • Use the current, I, from step 7. This is the total current:

  _____

  • For the first resistor, use the resistance, R, for the first resistor, found in step 4.

  _____

  • The equation for resistance is $R = V/I$.
  • To solve for voltage, you must rearrange the equation: $V = IR$.
  • What do you believe the voltage will be across the first resistor?

  _____

  • For the second resistor, use the resistance, R, for the second resistor, found in step 4.

  _____

  • Use the same equation you used to find the voltage across the first resistor.
  • What do you believe the voltage will be across the second resistor?

  _____

  • Use the circuit you built in step 7.
  • Use the multimeter. What is the voltage for the first resistor in the circuit you made?

  _____

  • Was your prediction correct?

  _____

  • Use the multimeter. What is the voltage for the second resistor in the circuit you made?

  _____

  • Was your prediction correct?

  _____

| Constructing Electric Circuits *continued*

Circuits with Two Resistors in Parallel

9. Use the multimeter. Measure the total resistance across both resistors when they are connected in parallel.

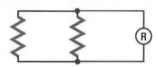

10. Predict the total current that will be in an entire circuit that has one battery and both resistors in parallel.

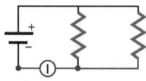

- The equation for resistance is $R = V/I$.
- To solve for current, you must rearrange the equation: $I = V/R$.
- Use the voltage, V, from one battery.

- Use the total resistance, R, that you measured in step 9.

- What do you believe the current in amps will be using one battery and both resistors in parallel, using the equation $I = V/R$?

- Build a circuit using both of your resistors in parallel and one battery.
- Use the multimeter. What is the current in amps in the circuit you made?

- Was your prediction correct?

Constructing Electric Circuits *continued*

11. Predict current that will be in each resistor individually.
    - Use the circuit with resistors in parallel you built in step 10.
    - The equation for resistance is $R = V/I$.
    - To solve for current, you must rearrange the equation: $I = V/R$.
    - You must solve for current for each of the resistors.
    - Use the voltage, V, from the battery you used in step 10.
    - What do you believe the current in amperes will be for the first resistor using the equation $I = V/R$?

    - Record your prediction for the first resistor.

    _____

    - What do you believe the current in amperes will be for the second resistor using the equation $I = V/R$?

    - Record your prediction for the second resistor.

    _____

ANALYSIS

1. **Describing Events** If you have a circuit that has one battery and one resistor, what happens to the current if you double the resistance? (**Hint:** To find the current it may be helpful to do a sample problem.)
   - Suppose you had a 1.5 V battery and a circuit with a resistance of 100 Ω.
   - The equation for resistance is $R = V/I$.
   - To solve for current, you must rearrange the equation: $I = V/R$.
$$I = (1.5 \text{ V})/(100 \ \Omega)$$
$$I = .015 \text{ A}$$
   - Double the resistance to 200 Ω, and solve for current.
$$I = (1.5 \text{ V})/(200 \ \Omega)$$
$$I = .0075 \text{ A}$$
   - Divide the current with a resistance of 100 Ω by the current with a resistance of 200 Ω to find the ratio.
$$(.0075 \text{ A})/(.015 \text{ A}) = .50 \text{ A, or } 50\%$$

2. **Describing Events** If you add a second, identical battery in series with the first battery, what happens to the current? (**Hint:** To find the current it may be helpful to do a sample problem.)
   - Suppose you had a 1.5 V battery and a circuit with a resistance of 100 Ω.
   - The equation for resistance is $R = V/I$.
   - To solve for current, you must rearrange the equation: $I = V/R$.
$$I = (1.5 \text{ V})/(100 \ \Omega)$$
$$I = .015 \text{ A}$$
   - Add a second 1.5 V battery in series with the first battery and solve for current.
   - The voltage is now 1.5 V + 1.5 V = 3 V.
   - Solve for current:
$$I = (3 \text{ V})/(100 \ \Omega)$$
$$I = .03 \text{ A}$$

   - Divide the current with 3 V by the current with 1.5 V to find the ratio.
$$(.03 \text{ A})/(.015 \text{ A}) = 2$$

3. **Describing Events** If you add a second resistor in parallel with the first resistor, will the current increase or decrease?

| Constructing Electric Circuits *continued*

COMMUNICATING YOUR RESULTS

4. **Drawing Conclusions** Suppose that you have a circuit that has one battery plus a 10 Ω resistor and a 5 Ω resistor in series.
   - Which resistor will have the greater voltage across it?
   - (**Hint:** 10 Ω is double the resistance of 5 Ω.)

_____

_____

_____

5. **Drawing Conclusions** suppose that you have a circuit that has one battery plus a 10 Ω resistor and a 5 Ω resistor in parallel.
   - Which resistor will have more current in it?
   - (**Hint:** Review your answer to step 11.)

_____

_____

EXTENSION
Suppose that someone tells you that you can make the battery in a circuit last longer by adding more resistors in parallel.
   - Will the battery drain more quickly if current is increased or if current is decreased?

_____

   - Will current increase or decrease if you add more resistors?

_____

   - Will a battery in a circuit last longer if more resistors are added in parallel?

_____

Name _____ Class _____ Date _____

Constructing Electric Circuits

The current that flows through an electric circuit depends on voltage and resistance. All these factors are dependent on one another. In this lab, you will make circuits using different configurations of resistors and batteries to see how the voltage and current depend on them.

WHAT YOU'LL DO

Construct parallel and series circuits.

Predict voltage and current by using the resistance law.

Measure voltage, current, and resistance.

WHAT YOU'LL NEED

- battery, dry-cell
- battery holder
- multimeter

- resistors (2)
- tape, masking
- wires, connecting (3)

SAFETY

PROCEDURE

Preparing for Your Experiment

1. In this laboratory exercise, you will use an instrument called a *multimeter* to measure voltage, current, and resistance. Your teacher will demonstrate how to use the multimeter to make each type of measurement.

2. As you read the steps listed below, refer to the diagrams for help making the measurements. Write down your predictions and measurements in your lab notebook. **CAUTION:** Handle the wires only where they are insulated.

Circuits with a Single Resistor

3. Using the multimeter, measure the resistance in ohms of one of the resistors.

_____

Write the resistance on a small piece of masking tape, and tape it to the resistor. Repeat for the other resistor.

_____

Constructing Electric Circuits *continued*

4. Use the resistance equation, $R = V/I$, to predict the current in amps that will be in a circuit consisting of one of the resistors and one battery. (**Hint:** You must rearrange the equation to solve for current.)

_____

5. Test your prediction by building the circuit.

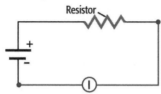

_____

Do the same for the other resistor.

_____

Circuits with Two Resistors in Series

6. Measure the total resistance across both resistors when they are connected in series.

_____

7. Using the total resistance that you measured, predict the current that will be in a circuit consisting of one battery and both resistors in series.

_____

Test your prediction.

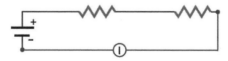

| Constructing Electric Circuits *continued*

8. Using the current that you measured, predict the voltage across each resistor in the circuit that you just built.

_____

Test your prediction.

Circuits with Two Resistors in Parallel

9. Measure the total resistance across both resistors when they are connected in parallel.

_____

10. Using the total resistance that you measured, predict the total current that will be in an entire circuit consisting of one battery and both resistors in parallel.

_____

Test your prediction.

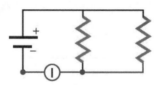

11. Predict the current that will be in each resistor individually in the circuit that you just built.

_____

Test your prediction.

Constructing Electric Circuits *continued*

ANALYSIS

1. **Describing Events** If you have a circuit consisting of one battery and one resistor, what happens to the current if you double the resistance?

_____

_____

_____

2. **Describing Events** What happens to the current if you add a second, identical battery in series with the first battery?

_____

_____

_____

3. **Describing Events** What happens to the current if you add a second resistor in parallel with the first resistor?

_____

_____

_____

COMMUNICATING YOUR RESULTS

4. **Drawing Conclusions** Suppose that you have a circuit consisting of one battery plus a 10 Ω resistor and a 5 Ω resistor in series. Which resistor will have the greater voltage across it?

_____

_____

_____

5. **Drawing Conclusions** Suppose that you have a circuit consisting of one battery plus a 10 Ω resistor and a 5 Ω resistor in parallel. Which resistor will have more current in it?

_____

_____

_____

Constructing Electric Circuits *continued*

EXTENSION

Suppose that someone tells you that you can make the battery in a circuit last longer by adding more resistors in parallel. Is this statement correct? Explain your reasoning.

Skills Practice Lab

DATASHEET C

Constructing Electric Circuits

The current that flows through an electric circuit depends on voltage and resistance. All these factors are dependent on one another. In this lab, you will make circuits using different configurations of resistors and batteries to see how the voltage and current depend on them.

WHAT YOU'LL DO

Construct parallel and series circuits.

Predict voltage and current by using the resistance law.

Measure voltage, current, and resistance.

WHAT YOU'LL NEED

- battery, dry-cell
- battery holder
- multimeter

- resistors (2)
- tape, masking
- wires, connecting (3)

SAFETY

PROCEDURE

Preparing for Your Experiment

1. In this laboratory exercise, you will use an instrument called a *multimeter* to measure voltage, current, and resistance. Your teacher will demonstrate how to use the multimeter to make each type of measurement.

2. As you read the steps listed below, refer to the diagrams of the circuits to help you in making the measurements. Write down your predictions and measurements in your lab notebook. **CAUTION:** Handle the wires only where they are insulated.

Circuits with a Single Resistor

3. Using the multimeter, measure the resistance in ohms of one of the resistors. Write the resistance on a small piece of masking tape, and tape it to the resistor. Repeat for the other resistor.

4. Use the resistance equation, $R = V/I$, predict the current in amps that will be in a circuit consisting of one of the resistors and one battery.

5. Test your prediction by building the circuit. Do the same for the other resistor.

| Constructing Electric Circuits *continued*

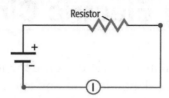

Circuits with Two Resistors in Series

6. Measure the total resistance across both resistors when they are connected in series.

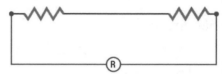

7. Using the total resistance that you measured, predict the current that will be in a circuit consisting of one battery and both resistors in series. Test your prediction.

8. Using the current that you measured, predict the voltage across each resistor in the circuit that you just built. Test your prediction.

Circuits with Two Resistors in Parallel

9. Measure the total resistance across both resistors when they are connected in parallel.

Constructing Electric Circuits *continued*

10. Using the total resistance that you measured, predict the total current that will be in an entire circuit consisting of one battery and both resistors in parallel. Test your prediction.

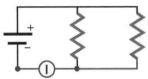

11. Predict the current that will be in each resistor individually in the circuit that you just built. Test your prediction.

ANALYSIS

1. **Describing Events** In a circuit consisting of one battery and one resistor, what happens to the current if you double the resistance?

_____

_____

_____

2. **Describing Events** What happens to the current if you add a second, identical battery in series with the first battery?

_____

_____

_____

3. **Describing Events** What happens to the current if you add a second resistor in parallel with the first resistor?

_____

_____

_____

COMMUNICATING YOUR RESULTS

4. **Drawing Conclusions** Suppose that you have a circuit consisting of one battery plus a 10 Ω resistor and a 5 Ω resistor in series. Which resistor will have the greater voltage across it?

_____

_____

_____

5. **Drawing Conclusions** Suppose that you have a circuit consisting of one battery plus a 10 Ω resistor and a 5 Ω resistor in parallel. Which resistor will have more current in it?

_____

_____

_____

EXTENSION

Suppose that someone tells you that you can make the battery in a circuit last longer by adding more resistors in parallel. Is this statement correct? Explain your reasoning.

Skills Practice Lab   OBSERVATION

Converting Wind Energy into Electricity

Teacher Notes

TIME REQUIRED
One lab period

SKILLS ACQUIRED
Constructing models
Experimenting
Predicting
Recognizing patterns

THE SCIENTIFIC METHOD

Make observations In the Procedure, students observe how changing parts of the system affects the system's operation and energy output.

Analyze the results In the Analysis, students look for patterns in their observations and offer explanations.

Draw conclusions In the Conclusions, students draw general conclusions about how the system should be set up to work best and predict how changes to the system would affect operation.

Communicate results In the Analysis and Conclusions, students communicate results by providing written answers to the questions.

MATERIALS

The pencils used to make the pinwheels should be round and smooth, not hexagonal. The pencils should be unsharpened (completely flat on the end opposite the eraser) and long enough to pass through the shoe boxes with at least 4 cm to spare.

You may use wooden dowels instead of pencils. In that case, you should use a thumbtack to carefully poke a hole in one end of each dowel before class. Do not leave this step for the students to do; they could easily poke or cut themselves. One advantage of using dowels is that they can be cut to any length so that they pass through the shoe boxes with ample length to spare.

SAFETY INFORMATION

Discuss all safety symbols and cautions with students.

Advise students to use caution when using the blow dryers. Blow dryers can become very hot when used for extended periods. Students should avoid touching the tip of the dryer to clothing, paper, or the turbines. Because blow dryers may blow dust or small objects, students should wear safety goggles during this experiment.

Converting Wind Energy into Electricity *continued*

Warn students that wire coils may become hot. (Because the current is low, the coils probably will not get very hot in this experiment, but it is a good message to convey for future experiments.)

Warn students about handling sharp objects, such as scissors and thumbtacks.

TECHNIQUES TO DEMONSTRATE

Show students a sample turbine so that they will know how to fold the poster board correctly.

If the students have not used voltmeters before, show them how to turn on a voltmeter and how to set the meter to the proper voltage range.

TIPS AND TRICKS

Balancing the turbine and shaft properly (step 11) is probably the most difficult—and most important—part of the Procedure. Help students who are having trouble with this step. The key is to have weight evenly distributed around the shaft and to have the magnet centered on the end of the shaft. Also, make sure that the edges of the holes through the box are smooth.

Name _____ Class _____ Date _____

Converting Wind Energy into Electricity

Introduction

Electricity can come from many different sources. The electricity in your house comes from a power plant, which may generate electricity by harnessing energy from burning coal or natural gas, nuclear reactions, flowing water, or wind. The energy from any one of these sources can be converted into electrical energy, which can in turn be converted into other forms of energy. For example, an electric stove or a toaster turns electrical energy into heat that can be used for cooking. A lamp turns electrical energy into light.

In this lab, you will build a device to convert the energy in wind into electrical energy. The electrical energy will then be converted into light as the electricity powers a light-emitting diode (LED).

OBJECTIVES

Construct a device that uses wind energy to generate electricity.

Use the device to power a light-emitting diode (LED).

Describe how changing various parts of the system affects the generation of electricity.

MATERIALS

- alligator clips and wire (2)
- ALNICO cylindrical cow magnet
- blow dryer, 1,500 W, 60 Hz
- hole punch
- LED, 2.0 V
- metric ruler
- modeling clay
- pencil, round and unsharpened
- pipe cleaners (2)
- poster board, 10 cm × 10 cm
- PVC wire, 100 ft coil
- scissors
- shoe box
- thumbtack
- transparent tape
- voltmeter or multimeter

SAFETY

PROCEDURE

Building a Windmill

1. Use the ruler as a straight edge to draw two diagonal lines on the poster board. Each line should go from one corner to the opposite corner. Punch a hole in the center of the square (where the lines cross). Make a 5 cm cut from each corner of the square toward the center (along the lines).

2. Slide the eraser end of the pencil through the hole in the center of the square so that the eraser end of the pencil sticks out about 3 cm. Carefully bend one corner of the square toward the eraser. Be careful not to make a fold in the poster board. Then, work your way around the square by bending alternating corners in to the eraser until the poster board is in a pinwheel shape, as shown in **Figure 1.** Use a thumbtack to pin the four folded corners to the eraser. This step can be tricky, so be patient and be careful not to poke yourself with the tack. When you are finished, you should have a turbine on a shaft.

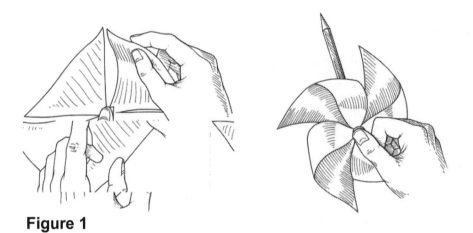

Figure 1

3. Push the back end of the turbine away from the eraser to create a lot of space in the turbine to catch wind. Securely tape the back end of the turbine to the pencil so that the shaft will turn when the turbine turns.

4. Place the box on the table so that the opening faces up. Carefully punch a hole in the long side of the shoebox, at least 8 cm above the table. Punch another hole on the other long side of the box so that the holes are opposite one another.

5. Use tape to attach the box to the table, or place a weight inside the box. Slide the shaft through the two holes so that the turbine is near the box and the other end of the shaft sticks out the other side of the box.

Converting Wind Energy into Electricity *continued*

6. Wrap pipe cleaners around the pencil where it exits the box on both sides. Tape the pipe cleaners to the pencil to prevent the shaft from sliding when wind blows on the turbine. Blow on the turbine to make sure that the turbine and shaft turn freely.

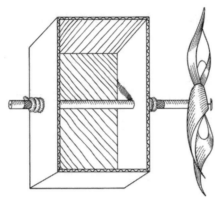

Figure 2

7. Tape the bar magnet to the end of the shaft opposite the turbine so that the shaft and magnet form a **T**, as shown in **Figure 3.** The two poles of the magnet should stick out to the left and right.

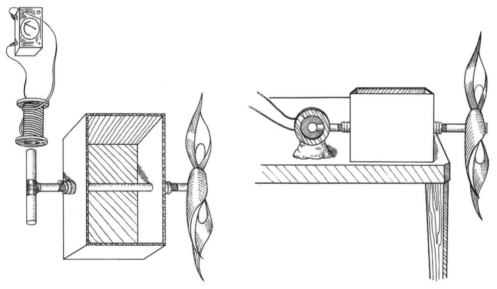

Figure 3

8. Place the coiled wire beside the magnet. Point the magnet's pole to the center of the coil. Place the coil on a base of modeling clay to hold the coil in position. Use the modeling clay to adjust the height of the coil so that the center of the coil is the same height as the magnet when it points to the coil. (The center of the coil should be at the same height as the shaft, about 8 cm above the table.)

Generating Electricity

9. Find the two loose ends of the wire. One wire is inside the coil, and the other wire is outside the coil. Tape the outside of the coil so that it does not unravel. Connect each loose wire end to a separate alligator clip and wire assembly. Clip the loose end of each alligator clip and wire assembly to a different voltmeter terminal.

10. Direct the blow dryer on the turbine. For best results, hold the blow dryer at an angle, as shown in **Figure 4.** Do not point directly at the center of the turbine but at one of the blades from the side. Be careful not to touch the turbine with the blow dryer.

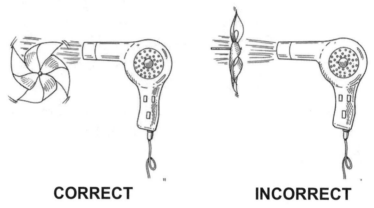

CORRECT   **INCORRECT**

Figure 4

11. For the windmill to work properly, the turbine and shaft must not wobble when they spin. You must also have a good connection between the wires, and the wire coil must be very close to the magnet. If the magnet or shaft wobbles as it spins, adjust the magnet so that it is centered on the end of the shaft. Also, adjust the pipe cleaners around the pencil; a slight movement can change how much the magnet wobbles. Be patient; the alignment must be exact for the windmill to produce electrical energy.

12. Once the turbine seems to be balanced and the coil seems to be positioned properly, direct the blow dryer on the turbine again and read the voltage on the voltmeter.

13. If the voltmeter reads less than 1 V, turn off the blow dryer. Check the connections to the coil and to the voltmeter. Make sure that there are no breaks in the insulation on the wire. Adjust the wire spool and the spinning magnet so that they are as close together as possible without touching. Direct the blow dryer on the turbine again. If the voltage is still less than 1 V, move the coil to slightly different positions while the turbine is spinning to try to get a higher voltage. Be careful not to let the coil touch the magnet while the magnet is spinning.

Converting Wind Energy into Electricity *continued*

Using Electricity to Light an LED

14. Once the voltmeter consistently reads over 1 V, turn off the blow dryer. Disconnect the voltmeter, and clip the alligator clips and wire assembly to each wire of an LED.

15. Direct the blow dryer on the turbine again. You should see the LED glow.

16. Move the blow dryer so that it points to the turbine at different angles. Observe how the brightness of the LED is affected.

17. While the LED is glowing, move the coil around so that the shaft points straight toward the center of the shaft. Observe how the brightness of the LED is affected.

18. When you are finished, take apart your windmill and put all supplies back in their proper place.

ANALYSIS

1. **Describing events** Starting with the wind from the blow dryer, list as many forms of energy as you can in the system you have built. Your list should have at least three forms of energy.

_____

_____

_____

_____

2. **Recognizing patterns** What happened to the brightness of the LED when you moved the blow dryer away from the position shown in Figure 4?

_____

_____

_____

3. **Explaining events** Why did moving the blow dryer change the brightness of the LED?

_____

_____

_____

_____

4. **Describing events** What happened to the brightness of the LED when you moved the coil in step 17?

_____

_____

_____

_____

CONCLUSIONS

1. **Drawing conclusions** Based on your observations, in what position should the coil be relative to the spinning magnet in order to produce the most electricity?

_____

_____

_____

_____

2. **Making predictions** Would the LED still glow if you turned the magnet so that it pointed straight out from the shaft?

_____

_____

_____

_____

3. **Drawing conclusions** Based on your observations, in what position should the blow dryer be relative to the turbine in order to produce the most electricity?

_____

_____

_____

_____

| Converting Wind Energy into Electricity *continued*

EXTENSIONS

1. **Building models** In a real-world situation, the wind blowing on a windmill does not always come from the same direction. How could you modify your windmill design to solve this problem?

_____

_____

_____

_____

_____

2. **Building models** In a real-world situation, the wind does not always blow enough to turn a windmill. What could be added to a windmill system to ensure a steady supply of electricity when the wind stops blowing (at least for a while)?

_____

_____

_____

_____

_____

Skills Practice Lab

CBL PROBEWARE

How the Length of a Conductor Affects Resistance

Teacher Notes

TIME REQUIRED
One lab period

SKILLS ACQUIRED
Experimenting
Identifying patterns
Interpreting
Organizing and analyzing data
Constructing models
Communicating

RATING

Easy ←——— 1   2   3   4 ——→ Hard

Teacher Prep–2
Student Set-Up–1
Concept Level–2
Clean Up–2

THE SCIENTIFIC METHOD

Analyze the results Analysis questions 1, 3, 4, 5, and 6 require students to calculate resistances and analyze their results

Draw conclusions Conclusions question 7 asks students to draw conclusions about the resistances of different materials.

Communicate results Extensions question 1 asks students to research and present information about different types of wires.

MATERIALS

If possible, have a voltage and a current probe, a dual channel amplifier, a CBL, and a graphing calculator connected for each group ahead of time. The calculators should be loaded with the Vernier PHYSCI program.

Make a 2 percent NaCl solution by dissolving 20 g of table salt (sodium chloride) in enough deionized water to make 1 L. Each group should fill its tray to a depth of about 0.5 cm.

If possible, provide plastic metric rulers so that they can be placed in the bottoms of the trays to measure the distance between the nails.

For best results, make sure the batteries you provide are either new or fully charged.

Make sure that the iron nails you provide are long enough so that the heads of the nails can be connected to a wire while the tips of the nails are in the saltwater solution.

SAFETY CAUTIONS

Discuss all safety symbols and cautions with students.

Students should wear safety goggles, gloves, and laboratory aprons while performing this experiment.

Remind students that wires that are conducting electricity can become very hot. Students should connect the battery only for short periods of time and immediately disconnect the battery after collecting data.

The sodium chloride solutions can be washed down the drain with plenty of water, provided your school drains are connected to a sanitary sewer system with a treatment plant. Make sure that students wash their hands when they are done with the experiment.

TECHNIQUES TO DEMONSTRATE

During the experiment, students may observe gas bubbles forming on one nail and the other nail oxidizing. You might want to discuss with them the way bleach is made commercially from salt water. This reaction is shown below.

$$\text{NaCl (dissolved)} \xrightarrow{\text{electric current}} \text{NaOCl (dissolved)} + \text{H}_2 \text{ (gas)}$$

TIPS AND TRICKS

Having two to four students in each lab group works best.

In step 10, when helping students assemble their circuits, make sure that the wires are making good contact everywhere in the circuit and that the nails are making good contact with both the wires and the salt water. Students might want to clip the nails to the plastic tray so that they stay upright.

Skills Practice Lab **CBL PROBEWARE**

How the Length of a Conductor Affects Resistance

Introduction

For power companies that must transmit electrical energy over very long distances along power lines, knowing the resistance of the wires that transmit this energy is very important. If the resistance is known, one can calculate the power lost in transmission to each house—whether that house is one block or 80 km (50 mi) away from the power company. Imagine that you have been hired by the power company to determine how increasing the length of a conductor affects the resistance of the entire circuit.

OBJECTIVES

Measure the current and voltage of a circuit several times, changing the length of one of the conductors in the circuit each time.

Calculate the resistance of the circuit.

Make a graph of your data to determine how increasing the length of one of the conductors in a circuit affects the resistance of the circuit.

MATERIALS

- 6-V battery
- CBL
- dual channel amplifier
- graph paper (optional)
- iron nails
- metric ruler
- 2% NaCl solution
- shallow plastic tray about 30 cm long
- TI graphing calculator and black link cable
- voltage and current probes (and adapter cables)
- 3 wires with alligator clips on each end

SAFETY

FINDING OUT MORE INFORMATION

For most conductors, the resistance of a circuit is related to voltage and current as described by Ohm's Law.

$$\text{current} = \frac{\text{voltage}}{\text{resistance}}$$

| How the Length of a Conductor Affects Resistance *continued*

Voltage is measured in volts (V), resistance is measured in ohms (Ω), and current is measured in amperes (A). If the current and the voltage of a circuit are known, you can rearrange Ohm's Law to calculate the resistance, as shown below.

$$\text{resistance} = \frac{\text{voltage}}{\text{current}}$$

COMING UP WITH A PLAN

To examine how increasing the length of a conductor affects resistance, you have to be able to vary the conducting distance easily. What you can do is set up a circuit using a battery, three wires attached to alligator clips, and two iron nails sitting in a tray of salt water (NaCl solution). The salt water will complete the circuit by conducting electricity between the two nails.

To increase the conducting distance, you can move the nails farther apart. Each time you move the nails, you can measure the current and the voltage of the circuit. Then you can use these values to calculate the resistance of the circuit.

PROCEDURE

1. Use the table below to record your data.

CIRCUIT DATA

Distance between nails (cm)	Voltage (V)	Current (A)	Resistance (Ω)
2			
4			
8			
12			
16			
20			
24			
28			

SETTING UP THE CBL SYSTEM

2. Plug the DIN 1 cable of the dual channel amplifier into the Channel 1 input of the CBL. Plug the DIN 2 cable into the Channel 2 input of the CBL. Plug the current probe into the PROBE 1 input of the dual channel amplifier. Plug the voltage probe into the PROBE 2 input of the dual channel amplifier.

3. Connect the CBL to the graphing calculator by plugging the black link cable into the base of each unit. Turn on both the CBL and the calculator. Press PRGM on the calculator, and select the PHYSCI program.

4. Go to the MAIN MENU, and select SET UP PROBES. Enter "2" as the number of probes. Select C-V CURRENT from the SELECT PROBE menu. Enter "1" as the channel number, and select USE STORED from the CALIBRATION menu.

How the Length of a Conductor Affects Resistance *continued*

5. With the current probe not connected to the circuit, press ENTER to zero the probe.

6. Select C-V VOLTAGE from the SELECT PROBE menu. Enter "2" as the channel number, and select USE STORED from the CALIBRATION menu.

7. Connect the two alligator clips from the voltage probe together. Press ENTER to zero the probe.

8. From the MAIN MENU, select COLLECT DATA. Select MONITOR INPUT from the DATA COLLECTION menu. Both current and voltage readings will be displayed on the calculator.

ASSEMBLING THE CIRCUIT

9. Fill the shallow tray with a half-centimeter of 2% NaCl solution.

10. Use the figure below as a guide to assemble the circuit. All lines represent wires. Solid lines show the circuit you will be testing. Dotted lines show how current and voltage readings are transferred to the CBL and calculator.

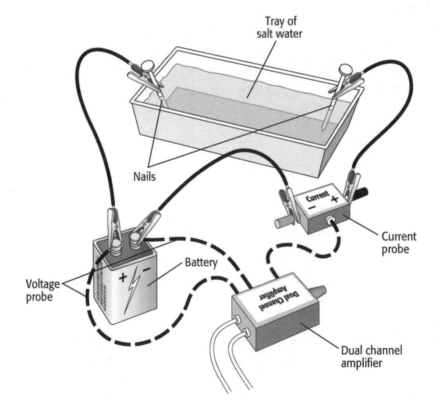

| How the Length of a Conductor Affects Resistance *continued*

MEASURING CURRENT AND VOLTAGE

11. Use a metric ruler to place the two nails in the solution 2 cm apart. Record both the current and voltage in the data table.

12. Move the nails apart each distance listed in the data table. Record the current and voltage each time in the table.

13. When you have finished, press "+" on the calculator. Then put away all of your materials, clean your work area, and wash your hands thoroughly.

ANALYSIS

1. Calculate the resistance of the circuit for each distance by using the following equation. Record your answers in the data table.

$$\text{resistance} = \frac{\text{voltage}}{\text{current}}$$

_____

_____

_____

_____

_____

2. Plot your data on the graph below. If you use your graphing calculator, sketch the graph here.

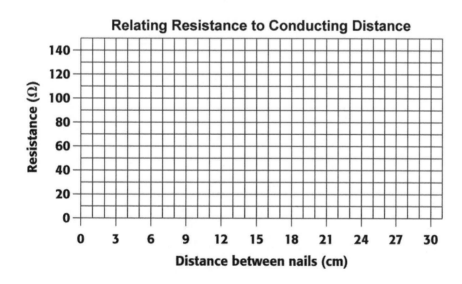

Relating Resistance to Conducting Distance

CONCLUSIONS

3. What happens to the resistance of the circuit as the length of one of the conductors (the salt water) increases?

_____

_____

_____

_____

4. Both the salt water and the wires in the circuit are conductors. Which do you think conducts electricity more easily? Explain your answer.

_____

_____

_____

_____

_____

5. Every conductor has some resistance. Compare the resistance of salt water with that of the wires in the circuit.

_____

_____

_____

_____

How the Length of a Conductor Affects Resistance *continued*

6. Suppose power is transmitted to your house from a transformer that is 45 m behind your house. The voltage supplied to your house is 110 V. If the power company guarantees a current of exactly 30 A at your breaker box (where the power enters your house), what is the maximum resistance per meter allowed in the power line to your house?

_____

_____

_____

_____

_____

_____

_____

7. How would your results be different if you had varied the length of one of the wires in the circuit instead of the conducting distance of the salt water?

_____

_____

_____

_____

_____

EXTENSION

1. Research the relative conductivity and cost of wires made from different metals. Summarize your findings in a poster that outlines the advantages and disadvantages of different types of wires.

Answer Key

Concept Reviews

SECTION: ELECTRIC CHARGE AND FORCE

1. Two unlike charges are attracted to each other.
2. The force is four times greater, or quadrupled. Alternatively, the difference between the forces is equal to three times the original force.
3. a. conductor
   b. conductor
   c. insulator
   d. conductor
   e. insulator
4. Both charges are positive; the charge on the left is greater.
5. a. upward
   b. downward
   c. The electron will have a greater acceleration because it is less massive than the proton.

SECTION: CURRENT

1. There must be a potential difference between the ends of the wire.
2. When an electric device is connected across the terminals of a battery, there is a potential difference across the device, and electric charges are accelerated by the electric field in the device.
3. Electric current is the rate at which electric charges move through a conductor. The units of current are amperes.
4. Resistance is due to internal friction slowing the movement of electrons through a conducting material. Resistance can be determined from the ratio of the voltage across a conductor to the current in the conductor using the relationship $R = V/I$.
5. 32 V
   $V = IR = (2.0\ \text{A})(16\ \text{ohms}) = 32\ \text{V}$
6. 1.8×10^{-2} A
   $I = V/R = 12\ \text{V}/650\ \Omega = 0.018\ \text{A}$
7. Superconductors are materials that have zero resistance when at or below their critical temperature. Conductors are materials in which electric charges can easily be transferred. Insulators are materials in which electric charges are not easily transferred. Semiconductors are between insulators and conductors in their electrical properties.

SECTION: CIRCUITS

1. battery (1); switch (2); resistors (5) (two are light bulbs)
2. The 20-amp fuse would give greater protection because it would melt at a lower value of current.
3. In a series circuit, there is only one path for electric charge. So current is the same everywhere throughout a series circuit. The voltage across each device in a series circuit may be different. In a parallel circuit, there is more than one conducting path. The voltage across each device is the same, but the current in each device can be different.
4. 53 W
   $P = IV (2.2\ \text{A})(24\ \text{V}) = 53\ \text{W}$
5. 0.33 A
   $I = P/V = (4.0\ \text{W})/(12\ \text{V}) = 0.33\ \text{A}$
6. $3.1 \times 10^2\ \Omega$
   $R = P/I^2 = (45\ \text{W})/(0.38\ \text{A})^2 = 310\ \Omega$
7. Answers may vary. They are connected in parallel, so they have the same voltage across them; therefore, the resistance of each appliance determines the current in the appliance. Alternatively, if one appliance does not work, the others will still be able to function if they are connected in parallel.

Math Skills

RESISTANCE

1. $V = IR = (15.6\ \text{A}) \times (7.7\ \Omega) = 120\ \text{V}$
2. $V = IR = (0.75\ \text{A})(6.4\ \Omega) = 4.8\ \text{V}$
3. $V = IR = (4.66\ \text{A})(25.0\ \Omega) = 116\ \text{V}$
4. $V = IR = (9.80\ \text{A})(12.2\ \Omega) = 120\ \text{V}$
5. $V = IR = (1.3\ \text{A})(3.5\ \Omega) = 4.6\ \text{V}$

   $$V_{battery} = \frac{V}{3} = \frac{4.6\ \text{V}}{3} = 1.5\ \text{V}$$
6. $I = \dfrac{V}{R} = \dfrac{12\ \text{V}}{4.1\ \Omega} = 2.9\ \text{A}$
7. $I = \dfrac{V}{R} = \dfrac{120\ \text{V}}{(8.0\ \Omega)25} = 0.60\ \text{A}$
8. $I = \dfrac{V}{R} \doteq \dfrac{115\ \text{V}}{24.0\ \Omega} = 4.79\ \text{A}$

9. $I = \dfrac{V}{R} = \dfrac{115\ \text{V}}{22\ \Omega} = 5.2\ \text{A}$

10. $R = \dfrac{V}{I} = \dfrac{120.0\ \text{V}}{0.520\ \text{A}} = 231\ \Omega$

11. $R = \dfrac{V}{I} = \dfrac{116\ \text{V}}{0.647\ \text{A}} = 179\ \Omega$

12. $I = \dfrac{V}{R}$ $I_{150} = \dfrac{120.0\ \text{V}}{96.0\ \Omega} = 1.25\ \text{A}$

$I_{300} = \dfrac{120.0\ \text{V}}{48.0\ \Omega} = 2.50\ \text{A}$

$I_{500} = \dfrac{120.0\ \text{V}}{29.0\ \Omega} = 4.14\ \text{A}$

13. $V = IR$

$(0.0050\ \text{A}) \times (1.0 \times 10^5\ \Omega) = 5.0 \times 10^2\ \text{V}$

$(0.0100\ \text{A}) \times (1.0 \times 10^5\ \Omega) = 1.0 \times 10^3\ \text{V}$

$(1.0\ \text{A}) \times (1.0 \times 10^5\ \Omega) = 1.0 \times 10^5\ \text{V}$

14. $R = \dfrac{V}{T} = \dfrac{115\ \text{V}}{3.0\ \text{A}} = 38\ \Omega$

$I = \dfrac{V}{R} = \dfrac{220\ \text{V}}{38\ \Omega} = 5.8\ \text{A}$

ELECTRIC POWER

1. $I = \dfrac{P}{V} = \dfrac{45\ \text{W}}{12\ \text{V}} = 3.8\ \text{A}$

$I = \dfrac{P}{V} = \dfrac{65\ \text{W}}{12\ \text{V}} = 5.4\ \text{A}$

2. $I = \dfrac{P}{V} = \dfrac{1250\ \text{W}}{240\ \text{V}} = 5.2\ \text{A}$

$I = \dfrac{P}{V} = \dfrac{2100\ \text{W}}{240\ \text{V}} = 8.8\ \text{A}$

3. $I = \dfrac{P}{V} = \dfrac{200.0\ \text{W}}{115\ \text{V}} = 1.74\ \text{A}$

4. $I = \dfrac{P}{V} = \dfrac{3.36 \times 10^4\ \text{W}}{440\ \text{V}} = 76\ \text{A}$

5. $I = \dfrac{P}{V} = \dfrac{1.0 \times 10^5\ \text{W}}{2.5 \times 10^5\ \text{V}} = 0.40\ \text{A}$

6. $V = \dfrac{P}{I} = \dfrac{4.00\ \text{W}}{3.40 \times 10^{-2}\ \text{A}} = 118\ \text{V}$

7. $V = \dfrac{P}{I} = \dfrac{54\ \text{W}}{4.5\ \text{A}} = 12\ \text{V}$

8. $V = \dfrac{P}{I} = \dfrac{1.85 \times 10^5\ \text{W}}{7.4\ \text{A}} = 2.5 \times 10^4\ \text{V}$

9. $V = \dfrac{P}{I} = \dfrac{6.0 \times 10^{13}\ \text{W}}{8.0 \times 10^6\ \text{A}} = 7.5 \times 10^6\ \text{V}$

10. $V = \dfrac{P}{I} = \dfrac{1.06 \times 10^4\ \text{W}}{16.3\ \text{A}} = 6.50 \times 10^2\ \text{V}$

11. $P = VI = (120\ \text{V}) \times (5.83\ \text{A})$
    $= 7.0 \times 10^2\ \text{W}$

12. $P = VI\ (120\ \text{V}) \times (12\ \text{A}) = 1.4 \times 10^3\ \text{W}$

13. $P = VI\ (116\ \text{V}) \times (0.62\ \text{A}) = 72\ \text{W}$

14. $P = VI = V\left(\dfrac{V}{R}\right) = \dfrac{(720\ \text{V})^2}{0.30\ \Omega}$

$= 1.7 \times 10^6\ \text{W}$

15. $I = \dfrac{P}{V} = \dfrac{7.50 \times 10^4\ \text{W}}{114\ \text{V}} = 658\ \text{A}$

16. $P = VI = V\left(\dfrac{V}{R}\right)$

$P_1 = \dfrac{(120.0\ \text{V})^2}{18.0\ \Omega} = 8.00 \times 10^2\ \text{W}$

$P_2 = \dfrac{(120.0\ \text{V})^2}{24.0\ \Omega} = 6.00 \times 10^2\ \text{W}$

$P_3 = \dfrac{(120.0\ \text{V})^2}{192\ \Omega} = 75.0\ \text{W}$

$P_{total} = P_1 + P_2 + P_3$
$= (8.00 \times 10^2\ \text{W}) + (6.00 \times 10^2\ \text{W})$
$+ (75.0\ \text{W}) = 1.48 \times 10^3\ \text{W}$

17. $P = VI = (1.65 \times 10^4\ \text{V}) \times (7.37 \times 10^3\ \text{A})$
    $= 1.22 \times 10^8\ \text{W}$

18. energy loss $= I^2 R = \left(\dfrac{P}{V}\right)^2 R$

energy loss
$= \left(\dfrac{5.00 \times 10^5\ \text{W}}{2.50 \times 10^2\ \text{V}}\right)^2 \times (1.00 \times 10^5\ \Omega)$
$= 4.00 \times 10^{11}\ \text{W}$

energy loss
$= \left(\dfrac{5.00 \times 10^5\ \text{W}}{2.50 \times 10^5\ \text{V}}\right)^2 \times (1.00 \times 10^5\ \Omega)$
$= 4.00 \times 10^5\ \text{W}$

19. $PE = mgh$
    $= (980\ \text{kg}) \times (9.8\ \text{m/s}^2) \times (25\ \text{m})$
    $= 2.4 \times 10^5\ \text{J}$

$P = \dfrac{energy}{time} = \dfrac{2.4 \times 10^5\ \text{J}}{1\ \text{s}} = 2.4 \times 10^5\ \text{W}$

$V = \dfrac{P}{I} = \dfrac{2.4 \times 10^5\ \text{W}}{20.0\ \text{A}} = 1.2 \times 10^4\ \text{V}$

Cross-Disciplinary

CONNECTION TO SOCIAL STUDIES: INCANDESCENT LIGHT BULBS

1. Halogen bulbs last longer because they continually rebuild the filament.
2. Tungsten atoms evaporate because the filament is so hot.

INTEGRATING BIOLOGY: ELECTRIC EELS

1. Yes. The longer the eel, the more electroplaques it would contain in its body. Similar to batteries, the more electroplaques, the more power.
2. Normal voltage is either 110 or 220. Electric eels can discharge about 5 times 110 or about 2.5 times 220.

3. Yes. An electric eel can discharge enough electricity to stun or possibly kill a human. River water is a good conductor of electricity. If the eel discharges enough electricity, the current could travel through the water and shock the person.

INTEGRATING CHEMISTRY: RECHARGEABLE NI-CD BATTERIES

1. Battery power is more useful when an appliance needs to be portable.
2. The electrons come from the cadmium anode.
3. Because regular batteries can be used only once, they must replaced when worn out. Rechargeable batteries cost only pennies to recharge, so replacing single-use batteries is more expensive in the long run.

INTEGRATING HEALTH: RECORDING ELECTRICITY IN THE BRAIN

1. Brain waves show less intense activity when you relax.
2. During an epileptic seizure, brain waves show more intense activity.
3. Neurons send electrical signals using chemicals.

REAL WORLD APPLICATIONS: ELECTRIC SHOCK: CAUTION!

1. No. The bird is not affected because it is not touching the ground. The children are touching the ground, so picking up the line would give them an electric shock.
2. The ground wire provides a path for electricity—other than through the person using the tool—in case the tool malfunctions.
3. No. The metal dryer is a good conductor. If the wire is in contact with the dryer, the dryer will be part of the circuit and will be charged. If you touch the door, you can act as a path to ground for the current.

SCIENCE AND THE CONSUMER: BATTERY ISSUES

1. Rechargeable batteries are more economical because they last longer.
2. Answers may vary. Sample answer: Rechargeable, because fewer of them are needed.

3. Answers may vary. Sample answer: Call the local waste management office to get instructions on disposing of batteries.

Pretest

1. An atom is made up of protons (positively charged particles), neutrons (neutral particles), and electrons (negatively charged particles). The protons and neutrons make up the dense nucleus of the atom. Electrons are the outermost particles.
2. A good conductor of electricity allows current to flow easily. A material with a high resistance does not allow current to flow.
3. b
4. c
5. c
6. Your body picks up an electric charge as you move across the carpet.
7. A ball has gravitational potential energy when it is at the top of a hill. As it rolls down the hill, its gravitational potential energy is converted into kinetic energy. At the bottom of the hill it has only kinetic energy. The total amount of energy of the ball is the same throughout its path (neglecting friction).
8. Answers may vary. Answers should include three of the following: flashlight, smoke detector, laptop computer, doorbell, calculator, garage door opener

Quizzes

SECTION: ELECTRIC CHARGE AND FORCE

1. c	6. e
2. a	7. d
3. b	8. c
4. b	9. a
5. b	10. f

SECTION: CURRENT

1. d	6. b
2. d	7. c
3. c	8. b
4. a	9. a
5. c	10. a

SECTION: CIRCUITS

1. a	6. e
2. c	7. f
3. c	8. a
4. d	9. b
5. c	10. d

Chapter Tests

TEST A (5 POINTS PER ITEM)

1. c
2. a
3. c
4. b
5. a
6. c
7. b
8. a
9. b
10. c
11. a
12. d
13. c
14. When two materials are rubbed together, electrons can be transferred from one material to the other. The material that gets the electrons becomes negatively charged, and the material that loses the electrons becomes positively charged.
15. because the positive charge is twice as great as the negative charge
16. The electrical potential energy of a charge is determined by the position of the charge relative to the position of all other electrical charges.
17. 1.7 A
18. Only the first light bulb will light. The other two bulbs are beyond the open switch and, therefore, will not receive current.
19. series circuit
20. Parallel circuits; otherwise everything would have to be on for anything to be on. There may be series circuits within the system, however. For example, lights that can be operated from switches at either entrance to a room, or wall sockets that work only when a switch is in the on position, use series circuits.

TEST B (5 POINTS PER ITEM)

1. a
2. c
3. c
4. d
5. c
6. b
7. a
8. b
9. b
10. a
11. d
12. c
13. c
14. When a negatively charged object touches a neutral object, electrons can flow into the neutral object, making it negatively charged. When a positively charged object touches a neutral object, electrons can flow into the positively charged object, causing the neutral object to become positively charged.
15. The electric force between two objects is inversely proportional to the square of the distance between the objects. This means if the distance doubles, the force decreases by a factor of 4.
16. 18 V
17. Resistance is internal friction that slows the movement of electrons in a conductor.
18. No. Because the switch is open, there is not a closed-loop path for the electrons to follow.
19. parallel circuit
20. You have been negatively charged by friction because you have picked up electrons from the rug. As you reach for a metal object, electrons will move from your body to the object because of their difference in electrical potential energy, and you will experience a mild shock.

Standardized Test Practice

1. C
2. A
3. D
4. C

Inquiry Lab: A Simple Circuit

1. The bulb should light up when you connect the bottom of the bulb to one terminal of the battery and the side of the bulb's base to the other termindal of the battery. This configuration makes a closed circuit including the battery.
2. The bulb will not light under any other configuration. Other configurations will not work because they are not closed circuits or the circuit does not include the battery.

Quick Lab: Charging Objects

ANALYSIS

1. The plastic comb and the tissue paper are insulators.

2. Negative charges are transferred from my hair to the comb making the comb negatively charged. When the comb is held near the tissue paper, molecules in the tissue paper are polarized, producing an induced positive charge on the surface nearest the comb and an induced negative charge on the surface farthest from the comb. As a result, the pieces of tissue paper are electrically attracted to the comb.

3. If I held the comb near my hair, my hair would be attracted to the comb.

Quick Lab: Using a Lemon as a Cell

ANALYSIS

1. Answers may vary depending on the metals used as electrodes. Larger electrodes will produce greater current. Consult an electrochemical series to determine which pair of electrodes should produce the greatest current.

2. Answers may vary.

Inquiry Lab: How Can Materials Be Classified by Resistance?

ANALYSIS

1. The conductivity tester lights up.

2. The iron nail, copper wire, aluminum nail, and brass key were good conductors. The glass stirring rod, wooden dowel, chalk, cardboard, plastic utensil, and cork were poor conductors.

3. Good conductors have low resistance and allow charges to pass through, while good insulators have high resistance.

Chapter Lab: Constructing Electric Circuits

DATASHEETS A, B, & C
Procedure

3. The resistances should be about 100 Ω and 200 Ω.

4. $I = \dfrac{V}{R} = (1.5\,\text{V}) / (100\,\text{W}) = 0.015\ \text{A}$ in the 100 Ω circuit

$I = \dfrac{V}{R} = (1.5\,\text{V}) / (200\,\text{W}) = 0.0075\ \text{A}$ in the 200 Ω circuit

5. About 0.015 A should be in the 100 Ω circuit and 0.0075 A should be in the 200 Ω circuit.

6. The total resistance should be about 300 Ω.

7. $I = \dfrac{V}{R} = (1.5\,\text{V}) / (300\,\text{W}) = 0.005\ \text{A}.$

The total current should be about 0.005 A.

8. $V = IR = (0.005\ \text{A})(100\ \Omega) = 0.5\ \text{V}.$ The voltage should be about 0.5 V across the 100 Ω resistor.

$V = IR = (0.005\ \text{A})(200\ \Omega) = 1.0\ \text{V}.$ The voltage should be about 1.0 V across the 200 Ω resistor.

9. The total resistance should be about 67 Ω.

10. $I = \dfrac{V}{R} = (1.5\,\text{V}) / (67\,\text{W}) = 0.022\ \text{A}.$

The total current should be about 0.022 A.

11. $I = \dfrac{V}{R} = (1.5\,\text{V}) / (100\,\text{W}) = 0.015\ \text{A}.$

About 0.015 A should be in the 100 Ω resistor.

$I = \dfrac{V}{R} = (1.5\,\text{V}) / (200\,\text{W}) = 0.075\ \text{A}.$

About 0.0075 A should be in the 200 Ω resistor.

Analysis

1. The current will be half as much as the original current.

2. The total current will be double the original current.

3. The total current will increase.

Communicating Your Results

4. The 10 Ω resistor will have the greater voltage across it.

5. The 5 Ω resistor will have more current in it.

Extension

No, adding more resistors will increase the amount of current in the circuit, which will drain the battery more quickly.

Observation: Converting Wind Energy into Electricity

ANALYSIS

1. Answers should include at least three of the following: wind energy (kinetic energy) from the blow dryer; mechanical kinetic energy of the turbine, shaft, and/or magnet; electromagnetic energy in the spinning magnet; electrical energy in the coil and wires; and light (electromagnetic energy) from the LED.

2. In most cases, moving the blow dryer away from the position shown in the figure causes the LED to dim. In some cases, moving the blow dryer may cause the LED to glow brighter.

3. In different positions, the blow dryer makes the turbine spin at different speeds. The faster the turbine spins, the brighter the LED glows (because there is more energy in the system).

4. The LED grew dimmer or stopped glowing.

CONCLUSIONS

1. To generate the most electricity, the coil should be close to the magnet and perpendicular (at a right angle) to the plane of the magnet's rotation.

2. no

3. Answers may vary. In most cases, students should find that the blow dryer works best if it is close to the turbine and pointed toward the turbine at an angle.

EXTENSIONS

1. You could put the windmill on a rotating base so that the windmill can be turned toward the wind. You could also add a rudder to the back of the windmill so that the windmill would turn automatically.

2. You could attach a rechargeable battery to the coil. When the wind blows, the battery charges. When the wind stops blowing, the energy stored in the battery can be used to generate electricity.

CBL Probeware: How the Length of a Conductor Affects Resistance

PROCEDURE

CIRCUIT DATA

Distance between nails (cm)	Voltage (V)	Current (A)	Resistance (Ω)
2	5.478	0.08536	64.18
4	5.506	0.07976	69.03
8	5.749	0.06577	87.41
12	5.562	0.06017	92.44
16	5.562	0.05621	98.95
20	5.462	0.05201	105.0
24	5.471	0.04758	115.0
28	5.562	0.04618	120.4

ANALYSIS

1. Answers will vary. The calculation for a distance of 2 cm between the nails is shown below. Answers for all the distances are listed in the table above.

$$\text{resistance (2 cm)} = \frac{5.478 \text{ V}}{0.08536 \text{ A}}$$

$$= 64.18 \text{ Ω}$$

2.

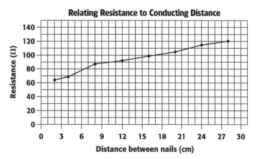

CONCLUSIONS

3. As the conducting length of the salt water is increased (the distance between the two nails is increased), the resistance of the circuit also increases.

4. The wires conduct electricity more easily than the salt water. The Na^+ and Cl^- ions in the solution are able to spread out more than electrons that are confined to a thin wire. Also, the solution may be less conductive in some areas due to the ions' mobility.

---

5. The salt water has a greater resistance than the wires in the circuit for the same reasons discussed in item 4.

6. The maximum resistance per meter allowed to the house can be found by solving the following equations:

$$\text{maximum resistance} = \frac{110\text{ V}}{30\text{ A}}$$

$$= 3.7\ \Omega$$

maximum resistance per meter =

$$\frac{3.7\ \Omega}{45\ m} = 0.082\ \Omega/\text{m}$$

This means that the resistance per meter cannot be greater than 0.082 Ω/m.

7. Because wires are such good conductors, varying the length of one of them in the circuit would not produce a noticeable change in the resistance of the circuit.

EXTENSION

1. Students can consult a wire supplier or use the Internet to do their research. Their posters should summarize the advantages and disadvantages of different kinds of wire.